THE LIFE
of
JESUS

igloo

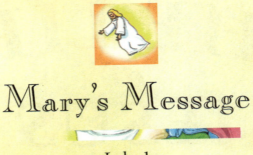

Mary's Message

Luke 1

Many years ago there lived a young girl called Mary. She was born in a village called Nazareth which was tucked away in the hills of Galilee.

Mary was very happy. She was engaged to be married to a carpenter called Joseph who also lived in the village.

One evening, as Mary sat quietly in her room, a blinding light suddenly appeared. She put her hand up to her face to shield her eyes but, through her fingers, Mary could dimly make out a shimmering figure in the very centre of the light.

"Don't be afraid, Mary," said the figure. "I am Gabriel, an angel of God. I have come to give you a message."
The angel's voice was so beautiful that Mary lost all her fear.
"What message do you have for me?" she asked, calmly.
"I have come to tell you that you are going to have a baby," replied Gabriel.

"But I'm not even married yet," said Mary.

"The Holy Spirit will come down and God's power will rest upon you," said Gabriel. "You will have a baby and you must call him Jesus. And he will be the Son of God."

"I am God's servant," Mary said quietly. "God's wish is my desire."

She raised her head, only to find herself in an empty room.

The angel Gabriel had left as silently as he had come.

The Birth of Jesus

Luke 2

Mary and Joseph were married. They loved each other very much and were looking forward to the birth of their baby.

The happy couple started to prepare their home in Nazareth for the birth. Then they heard some news that would change everything: The Roman Emperor, Augustus, who ruled the land, had made a new law. The new law said that everyone who was not living in their place of birth had to return there to register for a new tax. Joseph was born in Bethlehem, so he and Mary had to go there straight away.

Joseph and Mary hurried, because the baby was due to be born very soon. They quickly gathered together some clothes, a few warm blankets and some food and water for the journey. They packed it all on their donkey and started out on the road to Bethlehem.

It was nightfall by the time they arrived, tired and hungry. Even worse, all the inns where they could have stayed were full. After searching for some hours, the only place where they could find shelter was an empty stable.

Joseph made the stable as comfortable as he could for his wife, who laid down to rest. Some time later, Mary gave birth to a little baby boy. She gave thanks for his safe delivery and called him Jesus, as the angel Gabriel had asked her to.

Three Wise Men

Mathew 2

One night, in a country far from Bethlehem, three wise men were riding their camels along a dusty road when they noticed
a new star in the sky. It seemed to shine brighter than all the rest. "This star is a sign," they said. "It means a new King has been born. We must follow the star and it will lead us to him."

The star led them to the city of Jerusalem where King Herod ruled. Herod had already heard of the birth of a special baby in Bethlehem. He had learned from his priests that the baby would grow up to be the King of the Jews. Herod was angry and jealous. He didn't want to lose his power, especially to a baby born in a lowly stable.

He asked to meet the three wise men.
"I hear you are going to Bethlehem to worship a baby who will grow up to be King," he said. "Please tell me exactly where you find him, so I may go and worship him too."
The three wise men agreed, and the next morning they set out on the road to Bethlehem.

That night they arrived at the stable. When they saw the baby Jesus, they knelt down in front of him and offered him gifts. They had brought gold, sweet frankincense and myrrh. After they had blessed the child, the three wise men went quietly away and camped in the hills outside Bethlehem.

The wise men had planned to go back to Jerusalem the next morning and tell King Herod where to find the baby Jesus.

But that night they had a dream. In the dream, an angel told them that if they told Herod where to find the baby boy, Herod would kill him. As dawn broke, they quickly packed their belongings onto their camels, and took a different road back to their own country. The road took them away from Herod.

At the same time, Joseph also had a dream. In it, an angel told him the baby Jesus was in great danger. When he woke, Joseph told Mary of his dream. A worried Mary said they should leave at once. Joseph hurriedly loaded their donkey while Mary wrapped the sleeping Jesus in warm blankets. Then they started out on a long long journey to a country called Egypt.

Joseph, Mary and Jesus lived in Egypt until King Herod died. Now that they were not in danger, they decided it was safe to return to Nazareth.
At long last, they were going home.

The Baptism of Jesus

Mathew 3, Mark 1, Luke 3, John 1

Mary had a cousin called Elizabeth, who had a son called John. John grew up to be a strong, healthy man who was devoted to God. Many people went to Galilee to hear him speak. He would tell them to always share their food and clothes with poor people who had few belongings of their own.

John would baptize the people who believed in God. He would take them to the nearby river Jordan and carefully pour a little water over their heads. This meant these people had been washed clean of their sins, and from that day on could start to lead new, good lives. John told his followers that one day a man would make himself known to them all.

"This man will be the true Lord," he said.

When Jesus was thirty years old he waved goodbye to Joseph and Mary and left Nazareth. He went to Galilee to seek out his cousin, John. Jesus had heard that John was teaching God's message, and wanted to be baptized by him.

As soon as John saw him, he recognized Jesus for being the true Son of God.

"I am not worthy to baptize you," he told Jesus. "It is you who should baptize me."

"Let us do God's will," replied Jesus, and walked into the river until the water was up to his waist.

John followed and, scooping up a little water in his hand, gently baptized Jesus. All of a sudden the sky opened and a white dove, who was the spirit of God, flew down and hovered over Jesus's head. Then God's voice rang out, saying:

"This is my dear Son and I am pleased with him."

Twelve Disciples

J esus was becoming famous throughout the land. Wherever he went, people flocked around to hear him speak of God. One day, he was speaking on the shores of the Sea of Galilee and, as usual, there was a large crowd pressing in on him so that they could hear every word.

Jesus was getting closer and closer to the water's edge. When he saw a fishing boat nearby, he asked the fishermen if they would take him a little way out to sea so the crowds could see him better. The fishermen were Andrew and his brother, Peter.

After he had finished speaking to the crowds, Jesus told Andrew and Peter to row out to deeper waters and cast their net.
"We've been fishing all night," they complained, "and we haven't even caught one fish!"
"Do as I tell you and you will be rewarded," Jesus replied.

The fishermen did as Jesus asked. When they hauled in their net, they were amazed to see it was so full of fish it was almost bursting! They called to their friends, James and John, who were fishing nearby, to help them take all the fish back to shore.

The fishermen were pleased with their catch but were frightened of Jesus's powers.

"Do not be scared," said Jesus, gently. "Come with me and I will make you fishers of men."